THE FOOD
AND DRINK

Interactive Quiz

Managing Editors: Simon Melhuish and Sarah Wells
Series Editor: Nikole G Bamford
Designer: Linley J Clode
Writer: Paul Lucas
Cover Design: Alan Shiner

Published by
The Lagoon Group
PO Box 311, KT2 5QW, UK
PO Box 990676, Boston, MA 02199, USA

ISBN: 1904797628

© LAGOON BOOKS 2004

www.intelliquestbooks.com

Printed in China

IntelliQuest

UNIQUE BOOK CODE	025

Instructions

First of all make sure you
have a Quizmo —

Find the book's unique code (this
appears at the top of this page).
Use the < and > buttons to
scroll to this number on the Quizmo
screen. Press the ⏎ button to enter
the code, and you're ready to go.

Use the < > scroll buttons to select
the question number you want to
answer. Press the Ⓐ, Ⓑ, Ⓒ, or Ⓓ
button to enter your chosen answer.

If you are correct the green light beside the
button you pressed will flash. You can then use
the scroll button to move on to another question.

If your answer is incorrect, the red light beside the button
you pressed will flash.

Don't worry, you can try again and again until you have the correct answer, OR move on to another question. (Beware: the more times you guess incorrectly, the lower your final percentage score will be!)

You can finish the quiz at any point — just press the ⬖ button to find out your score and rank as follows:

75% or above	You're an epicurean genius!
50% — 74%	You're a veritable gourmet!
25% — 49%	Not quite a masterchef yet — keep on tasting!
Less than 25%	Those tastebuds need a lot more exercise!

If you do press the ⬖ button to find out your score, this will end your session and you will have to use the ⬖ to start again!

HAVE FUN!

001

The Aztec name for an avocado was ahvacatl, which translates as what?

A Little brain

B Testicle

C Green egg

D Foul tears

002

What's the oldest known vegetable?

A Potato

B Cabbage

C Turnip

D Pea

003

What food was erroneously blamed for causing outbreaks of leprosy and syphilis in 17th century Europe?

A Potato

B Rhubarb

C Bacon

D Apple

– Food in History –

004

What did ancient Greek athletes rub on their bodies before participating in the games?

- **A** Onions
- **B** Tomatoes
- **C** Camel milk
- **D** Olive oil

005

Peckish Romans dined on which of the following?

- **A** Dogs
- **B** Cats
- **C** Mice
- **D** Worms

006

Montezuma, the Emperor of the Aztecs, was said to drink up to fifty cups of what a day?

- **A** Blood
- **B** Chocolate
- **C** Wine
- **D** Honey

– Blast from the Pasta –

007 During the Middle Ages, what was caudle?

A An alcoholic beverage given to those who were sick

B Frog soup

C A rudimentary anesthetic made from fermented elderberries

D A burning hot drink administered as a form of torture

008 What did the ancient Greeks award to the winners of sporting events?

A Oranges

B Olives

C Figs

D Celery

009 The oldest complete recipe book known dates back to when?

A 2400 BC

B AD 1657

C AD 933

D AD 62

– Food in History –

The oldest known recipe is for what?

- **A** Beer
- **B** Mammoth
- **C** Risotto
- **D** Bread

When swearing an oath, ancient Egyptians would place their right hands on what?

- **A** An onion
- **B** A fish
- **C** A jug of wine
- **D** A sack of juniper berries

Punters awaiting the services of Elizabethan prostitutes were served what to put them in a lusty mood?

- **A** Raw meat
- **B** Prunes
- **C** Chicken soup
- **D** Oysters

– Foodspeak –

013

According to GK Chesterton, the poets have been mysteriously silent on the subject of – what?

A Bananas

B Cheese

C Chocolate

D Toast

014

Who wrote: The cook was a good cook, as cooks go: and as cooks go, she went?

A PG Wodehouse

B Charles Dickens

C Oscar Wilde

D HH Munro

015

According to the wise Muppet Miss Piggy, you should never eat more than you can what?

A Lift

B See

C Afford

D Throw

– Tasty Quotations –

016

What did Jonathan Swift describe as a most delicious, nourishing, and wholesome food, whether stewed, roasted, baked, or boiled?

- **A** A one-year-old child
- **B** Dogs
- **C** Rats' brains
- **D** Nettles

017

Ernest Dowson warned: They are not long, the days of what?

- **A** Beer and kisses
- **B** Ale and song
- **C** Wine and roses
- **D** Love and yogurt

018

Who wrote: Candy is dandy but liquor is quicker?

- **A** Saki
- **B** Edward Lear
- **C** Osbert Sitwell
- **D** Ogden Nash

019

Who implored: Drink to me only with thine eyes, And I will pledge with mine; Or leave a kiss but in the cup, And I'll not look for wine.

- **A** William Shakespeare
- **B** Ben Jonson
- **C** Andrew Marvell
- **D** Christopher Marlowe

020

Whose dying wish was to decompose in a barrel of porter and have it served in all the pubs in Dublin?

- **A** James Joyce
- **B** Flann O'Brien
- **C** JP Donleavy
- **D** Brendan Behan

021

Who said: My advice if you insist on slimming: Eat as much as you like – just don't swallow it?

- **A** Spike Milligan
- **B** Groucho Marx
- **C** Harry Secombe
- **D** Dorothy Parker

In Hong Kong and Taiwan, what is sold under the name of fragrant meat?

022

A Dog meat

B Horse meat

C Anchovies

D Kentucky Fried Chicken

The Japanese traditionally eat fried chicken and strawberry shortcake on what day?

023

A New Year's Eve

B New Year's Day

C Christmas Eve

D Christmas Day

Which of these taste like nuts?

024

A Locusts

B Slugs

C Snails

D Caterpillars

025 Which of these taste like shrimp?

- **A** Ants
- **B** Bees
- **C** Grasshoppers
- **D** Bats

026 What do cactus worms taste like?

- **A** Fish
- **B** Beef
- **C** Pork
- **D** Strawberries

027 In 1973 a Swedish confectionery salesman elected to be buried in a coffin made of what?

- **A** Turkish Delight
- **B** Chocolate
- **C** Fudge
- **D** Caramel

– Weird Food Facts –

What color Is yak's milk?

028

- **A** Pink
- **B** White
- **C** Green
- **D** Yellow

What's the highest price ever paid for a corkscrew?

029

- **A** £5,000/$8000
- **B** £16,000/$25,600
- **C** £89,000/$142,400
- **D** £1,400,000/£2,240,000

What's unusual about the Gout du Noir restaurant in Paris?

030

- **A** It's underwater
- **B** It only opens once a year
- **C** Customers are served in total darkness
- **D** Every dish on the menu is horse meat

031 Which of these foods is an ingredient in dynamite?

  A Chili
  B Peanuts
  C Asparagus
  D Rhubarb

032 A popular dish in Asia is what?

  A Chicken's feet
  B Squirrel's claw
  C Dolphin's blowhole
  D Lizard's tail

033 What drink is reputed to be very good for cleaning diamonds?

  A Vodka
  B Coca-cola
  C Beer
  D Milk

– Weird Food Facts –

Certain types of bubble-gum contain small amounts of what?

034

- A Glass
- B Rubber
- C Cyanide
- D Lead

If you're feeling adventurous in Korea, you might want to try poshintang. It's a soup believed to be good for the complexion and made from what?

035

- A Dogs
- B Manure
- C Human blood
- D Termites

In Venezuela, when you plump for the calamares en su tinta, what will be served?

036

- A Goat's eyes wrapped in vine leaves
- B Baboon hearts in pastry
- C Scorpions on a bed of rice
- D Squid served in its ink

037 In Ecuador, of course, you'll want to sample the tronquito which is —?

- **A** Monkey pie
- **B** Bull's penis soup
- **C** A warm drink of crocodile blood
- **D** Llama gizzards

038 If you want to wash this down with a drink, be careful In rural Ecuador, the fermented maize drink chicha often contains an unhealthy amount of —?

- **A** Cocaine
- **B** Lead
- **C** Human saliva
- **D** Goat's urine

039 In Samoa? Peckish? Do try the —

- **A** Fried frog
- **B** Stewed snake
- **C** Roast rat
- **D** Baked bat

– Weird Food Facts –

040

Frank Buckland was a 19th Century naturalist who liked to experiment with unusual foods. He ate all of the following – but which did he describe as rather bitter?

- **A** Elephant's trunk
- **B** Roast giraffe
- **C** Panther chops
- **D** Earwigs

041

Frank Buckland's father William, on the other hand, was none too partial to which particular exotic food?

- **A** Kangaroo
- **B** Monkey
- **C** Mole
- **D** Humming bird

042

New York state's official muffin is what flavor?

- **A** Blueberry
- **B** Apple
- **C** Chocolate
- **D** Strawberry

043

Which of these means sausage and beans?

A Batons in blood

B Hounds on an island

C Logs in a lumpy river

D Turds in wind

044

If you asked for warts what would you most likely be served?

A Olives

B Peas

C Sweetcorn

D Beans

045

Shingles with a shimmy means —?

A Beans on toast

B Toast and jam

C Ham and eggs

D Doughnuts and a coffee

A bucket of cold mud means —?

046

- **A** Chocolate ice cream
- **B** Hot fudge sauce
- **C** Soup
- **D** Chocolate milk shake

Which of this is a slang term for butter?

047

- **A** Bile
- **B** Waste paste
- **C** Slab of sun
- **D** Axle grease

Cows are —?

048

- **A** Steaks
- **B** Milkshakes
- **C** Eggs
- **D** Hamburgers

049 If you asked a waitress for hamburgers, and then added 'make 'em cry' you'd be asking her to do what?

  A Make sure they were well-done

  B Serve them with onions

  C Serve them as quickly as possible

  D Insult them thoroughly

050 If you asked for zeppelins in fog you'd most likely end up with —?

  A Sausages in gravy

  B Sausages in beans

  C Sausages in mashed potatoes

  D A slap on the cheek

051 Eve with a lid on means what?

  A Surprise me

  B Cheesecake

  C Apple sauce

  D Apple pie

– Coffee Shop Slang –

A granita is a latte with what?

- **A** Extra sugar
- **B** Cinnamon
- **C** Melted chocolate
- **D** Frozen milk

Skinny means served with what?

053

- **A** Water
- **B** Semi-skimmed milk
- **C** Cream
- **D** Alcohol

A regular filter coffee is known as a what?

054

- **A** Drape
- **B** Drop
- **C** Drip
- **D** Dog

– Coffee Shop Slang –

055

A coffee with double cream and double sugar is called a what?

A Cake in a cup

B Fat Boy

C Super Bowl

D Mad Dog

056

If you ordered something wild how would it come?

A Ready to take away

B Without milk

C Decaffeinated

D With whipped cream

057

What is the name of the worlds costliest coffee? At $130 a pound it is made from the droppings of a marsupial that eats only the very best coffee beans. Plantation workers track them and scoop their precious poop.

A Tanzanian Peaberry

B Kopi Luwak

C Indian Monsooned Malabar AA Super Grade

D Colombian Supremo

What was originally sold as An Intellectual Beverage And Temperance Drink?

`058`

- A Lemonade
- B Coca-Cola
- C Bourbon
- D Tea

What was Colonel Sanders' first name?

`059`

- A Eric
- B Chuck
- C Harland
- D Beverley

How many herbs and spices are there in KFC's special chicken coating?

`060`

- A Over 100
- B 2
- C 9
- D 18

– Fast Food and Junk Food –

061 Approximately how many Coca-Colas are consumed worldwide per day?

A 600 million
B A million
C Around about 30
D Four trillion

062 McDonalds in New Delhi makes its burgers with what?

A Beef
B Mushrooms
C Pork
D Mutton

063 What did Louis Lassen invent in 1900?

A The Mars Bar
B Hot dog
C Chips
D Hamburger

– Fast Food and Junk Food –

Pizza originated in which city?

064

- **A** Naples
- **B** Rome
- **C** New York
- **D** Venice

What was the name of the 1930s comic strip used to advertise Pepsi Cola?

065

- **A** Cola The Koala
- **B** Pepsi and Pete
- **C** Pepsi The Penguin
- **D** Fizzy And Friends

Chocolate has been around for centuries, but milk chocolate was only invented in which year?

066

- **A** 1875
- **B** 1895
- **C** 1915
- **D** 1935

067 What did John Pemberton invent in 1886?

A Coca-Cola

B The ice cream cone

C The Snickers bar

D Pepsi Cola

068 What did Caleb Bradham invent in 1898?

A Popcorn

B The ice cream cone

C Pepsi Cola

D Dry roasted peanuts

069 What opened at 53 1/3 Spring Street in New York in 1905?

A First American fast food outlet

B First American diner

C First American pizzeria

D First American donut shop

– Fast Food and Junk Food –

Children in the US voted what food to be their favorite school lunch?

A Pizza

B Chicken nuggets

C Tacos

D Hamburgers

What was the original name of Pepsi Cola?

A Firefly

B Popsi Cola

C Brad's Drink

D Dr Bradley's Carbonated Vegetable Tonic

What was invented by an 11-year-old boy in 1905?

A Ice cream

B Popcorn

C The Popsicle

D Crisps/Potato chips

073

7-Up originally contained what?

A Cocaine
B Prozac
C Arsenic
D Lithium

074

In what year did the clown Ronald McDonald appear?

A 1911
B 1948
C 1963
D 1977

075

In Norway you can enjoy a McLak burger, made from what?

A Reindeer
B Salmon
C Yak
D Offal

Where were French Fries invented?

`076`

- **A** Belgium
- **B** France
- **C** England
- **D** USA

The largest commercially available pizza is 4 foot in diameter and can be ordered for $9999 from Paul Revere's Pizza in Iowa, USA. Just pick up the phone and ask them to send you over the —?

`077`

- **A** Shock And Awe Pizza
- **B** Big Paul Pizza
- **C** Homer's Pizza Dream
- **D** Ultimate Party Pizza

Bernard Jordaan Butler's pizza in Cape Town, South Africa, promise to deliver their pizza ANYWHERE. Corne Krige's was probably cold when it arrived, but then he did order it from —?

`078`

- **A** Moscow, Russia
- **B** San Francisco, USA
- **C** London, England
- **D** Sydney, Australia

079 What has American Donald Gorske eaten at least one of, every single day since 1972?

- **A** A Domino's pizza
- **B** A Big Mac
- **C** A Burger King Whopper
- **D** A bucket of Kentucky Fried Chicken

080 The largest pizza delivery of all time was taken by Little Caesar's pizzeria in the USA in 1998. It was for how many pizzas?

- **A** 29
- **B** 4,519
- **C** 13,386
- **D** 106

081 A curry house in Newcastle-upon-Tyne in the UK once delivered a vegetable biryani to a customer living where?

- **A** London, UK
- **B** New York, USA
- **C** Paris, France
- **D** Sydney, Australia

– Question Thyme –

What herb is mentioned in Hamlet as being for remembrance?

082

- **A** Basil
- **B** Chives
- **C** Rosemary
- **D** Lavender

The most expensive spice on earth is what?

083

- **A** Mace
- **B** Saffron
- **C** Bouquet Garni
- **D** Posh spice

What is saffron made from?

084

- **A** Oysters
- **B** Crocus flowers
- **C** Pearls
- **D** Seaweed

085 Comfrey was known in ancient times as what?

- **A** Cat's tail
- **B** Knucklewhite
- **C** Knitbone
- **D** Greek fire

086 Which of these herbs was NOT brought to Britain by the Romans?

- **A** Chives
- **B** Marjoram
- **C** Basil
- **D** Fennel

087 Which herb's name is derived from the French for little dragon?

- **A** Chervil
- **B** Tarragon
- **C** Borage
- **D** Comfrey

– Question Thyme –

What spice did the sailors in Henry VIII's navy take to cure wind?

- **A** Pepper
- **B** Cloves
- **C** Saffron
- **D** Paprika

Moss Curled and Green Velvet are both types of what?

- **A** Lavender
- **B** Fennel
- **C** Parsley
- **D** Bay leaves

Which herb is also known as wild marjoram?

- **A** Oregano
- **B** Basil
- **C** Chives
- **D** Nutmeg

091 Which liqueur has over 100 herbs in it?

- **A** Chartreuse
- **B** Tia Maria
- **C** Blue Curacao
- **D** Poteen

092 What herbs are found in a bouquet garni?

- **A** Mint, Lavender and Bay
- **B** Bay, Basil and Chives
- **C** Parsley, Mint and Oregano
- **D** Thyme, Bay and Parsley

093 Which of these measures the comparative heat of chilies?

- **A** The Scoville Scale
- **B** The Gresty Index
- **C** The Harper Index
- **D** The Rawringtomorra Scale

The hottest chili in the world is called the what?

094

- **A** Mulero
- **B** Bastarda
- **C** Habanero
- **D** El Bum Fuego

Which herb did the Romans think would keep them sober?

095

- **A** Mint
- **B** Oregano
- **C** Basil
- **D** Parsley

The nutmeg tree produces two spices: nutmeg, obviously, but what else?

096

- **A** Cloves
- **B** Mace
- **C** Paprika
- **D** Vanilla

097 Which part of the cinnamon tree is used to produce cinnamon spice?

A The leaves

B The roots

C The seeds

D The bark

098 Which spice comes from the dried flower buds of an evergreen tree native to Indonesia?

A Cloves

B Capers

C Juniper berries

D Paprika

099 What's the name of the root that flavors root beer?

A Sarsaparilla

B Tuber

C Ginger

D Faustinoasprilla

– Question Thyme –

What's the best selling spice in the world?

100

- **A** Paprika
- **B** Chili
- **C** Pepper
- **D** Curry powder

Tabasco sauce, made from peppers and fermented vinegar, was invented where?

101

- **A** Mexico
- **B** United States
- **C** England
- **D** India

Which spice was often used for bartering in The Middle Ages in Europe?

102

- **A** Pepper
- **B** Saffron
- **C** Mace
- **D** Cinnamon

103 What herb was worn by ancient Greeks during exams?

A Mint

B Chives

C Lavender

D Rosemary

104 What herb did the ancient Chinese cultures believe could cure a snake bite?

A Angelica

B Hyssop

C Chamomile

D Fennel

105 Which of these herbs does NOT belong to the mint plant family?

A Chicory

B Thyme

C Marjoram

D Oregano

Beef Wellington, named after The Duke of Wellington, consists of fillet steak wrapped in what?

106

- **A** Puff pastry
- **B** Filo pastry
- **C** Shortcrust pastry
- **D** Brown paper

The meringue dessert Pavlova was named after Anna Pavlova, a famous what?

107

- **A** Courtesan
- **B** Ballerina
- **C** Martyr
- **D** Poet

What cake is named after Queen Charlotte, wife of George III?

108

- **A** Peach Charlotte
- **B** Apple Charlotte
- **C** Plum Charlotte
- **D** Poor Charlotte

109

Savarin, named after the chef who first created it, is a fruit sponge flavored with what?

A Brandy

B Coffee

C Chocolate

D Rum

110

Peach Melba was named after a famous what?

A Soprano

B Dancer

C Prostitute

D Cyclist

111

Which of these composers had a dish of marzipan dipped in chocolate named after him?

A Mozart

B Handel

C Beethoven

D Bach

The word biscuit comes from the French, and means what?

- **A** Lightly-baked
- **B** First-dipped
- **C** Twice-cooked
- **D** Lastly-coated

Which of these gets its name from the Greek word for a pearl?

- **A** Asparagus
- **B** Mushroom
- **C** Mayonnaise
- **D** Margarine

Which of these does NOT get its name from an Aztec word?

- **A** Tomato
- **B** Yogurt
- **C** Avocado
- **D** Chocolate

115

The dish Vichyssoise was created to celebrate the opening of The Ritz Carlton Hotel roof garden in New York. What type of dish is it?

- **A** A lemon dessert
- **B** A savory snack
- **C** A cold soup
- **D** A fish salad

116

What's the main ingredient of Bombay duck?

- **A** Beef
- **B** Lamb
- **C** Fish
- **D** Duck

117

Which of these was NOT a slang term for gin in 18th Century England?

- **A** Widow's Tickle
- **B** Make Shift
- **C** Ladies' Delight
- **D** Cuckold's Comfort

Which of these is a French version of Curacao? 118

- **A** Tia Maria
- **B** Absinthe
- **C** Grand Marnier
- **D** Vermouth

Which of these did NOT originate in the US? 119

- **A** Russian Dressing
- **B** Chop Suey
- **C** Swiss Steak
- **D** Chicken Tikka

Vodka is Russian for what? 120

- **A** Water of fire
- **B** Essential
- **C** Little water
- **D** Lonely night

121

The Portuguese grape variety 'borrado das moscas' means what in English?

A Pig's eyes

B Grape of the Devil

C Fly droppings

D Fruit of the Saints

122

What was the name of the blind monk credited with inventing Champagne?

A Moet Chandon

B Dom Perignon

C Krug

D Laurent Perrier

123

The Japanese dish Sukiyaki means what in English?

A Grilled on a ploughshare

B Fried in bamboo shoots

C Baked alive

D Burned underwater

– You Say Tomato... –

Which of these is NOT another name for an eggplant?

- **A** Melanzana
- **B** Purpella
- **C** Garden egg
- **D** Aubergine

The dessert 'parfait' gets its name from the French word for what?

- **A** Softly
- **B** Clouds
- **C** Perfect
- **D** Snow

What type of food is associated with the immensely wealthy Rockefeller family?

- **A** Caviar
- **B** Oysters
- **C** Venison
- **D** Sausages

127

The French term for an apple turnover, Chausson Aux Pommes, means what in English?

- **A** Slipper with apples
- **B** Glove with apples
- **C** Boot with apples
- **D** House of the apples

128

Which of these is a potentially lethal Japanese fish dish?

- **A** Fugu
- **B** Pingu
- **C** Bugu
- **D** Killu

129

The world's first soda pop was called what?

- **A** Crowther's Tonic
- **B** Nephite Julep
- **C** Daisy's Summer Hat
- **D** Medicine 85

What do the French call lost bread?

130

- **A** Bread pudding
- **B** Toast
- **C** Doughnuts
- **D** Sandwiches

A popular Dutch dish made from beans is called what?

131

- **A** Bare breasts in the ocean
- **B** Lady's knees
- **C** Grandmothers kisses
- **D** Bare buttocks in the grass

Who invented the Manhattan cocktail?

132

- **A** The wife of President Ford
- **B** The mother of Winston Churchill
- **C** The daughter of Napoleon
- **D** The grandmother of Hillary Clinton

– What's in a Name –

133 **How did the Manhattan get its name?**

A The recipe was invented by Samuel J Manhattan

B The glass it was first served in was tall like a Manhattan skyscraper

C It was named after The Manhattan Club in New York

D It cost $1, or one Manhattan in the vernacular of the time

134 **Desert Gold, Redhaven and Elberta are all types of what?**

A Cocktails

B Liqueurs

C Grapes

D Peaches

135 **The Bloody Mary was named after Queen Mary – what's in it?**

A Gin and orange juice

B Whiskey and tomato juice

C Gin and cranberry juice

D Vodka and tomato juice

What does Haagen Daazs mean?

136

- **A** Ice cream
- **B** Cream Snow
- **C** Nothing – it's gibberish
- **D** Cream Of The Gods

SPAM gets its name from –

137

- **A** SPeciality hAM
- **B** SPiced hAM
- **C** Specially PAckaged Meat
- **D** Spiced Pork And Mutton

Linguine, a type of pasta, got its name from the Italian for what?

138

- **A** Little snails
- **B** Little tongues
- **C** Little worms
- **D** Little snakes

139

What did barmaid Betsy Flanagan allegedly invent?

- **A** The term cocktail
- **B** The Beer Mat
- **C** The Margarita
- **D** All of the above

140

Where was marzipan invented?

- **A** New Orleans
- **B** Milan
- **C** London
- **D** Salzburg

141

Won ton means what?

- **A** Swallowing a cloud
- **B** Swallowing a cow
- **C** Tasting the sky
- **D** Tasting colors

– Food for Thought –

About how many cherries does it take to make a cherry pie?

- **A** 30
- **B** 800
- **C** 100
- **D** 250

How many flowers must a hive of honey bees tap to make one pound of honey?

- **A** 10
- **B** 1000
- **C** 100,000
- **D** 2,000,000

How many miles does a hive of honey bees have to fly to make one pound of honey?

- **A** 200
- **B** 55,000
- **C** 1,000,000
- **D** 6,000,000

145

Roughly how many types of banana are there?

A A dozen

B 100

C 500

D 6,000

146

About how many gallons of milk does a cow produce in a year?

A 20

B 500

C 100

D 1,500

147

What temperature, in degrees Fahrenheit, is cow's milk when it comes out of a cow?

A 22

B 134

C 9

D 97

– Food for Thought –

About how many quarter pound hamburgers can be made from the average cow?

148

- **A** 3,000
- **B** 720
- **C** 140
- **D** 12

About how many gallons of milk does it take to make a gallon of ice cream?

149

- **A** 0.3
- **B** 1
- **C** 1.4
- **D** 20

About how many varieties of apples are known to exist?

150

- **A** 7,000
- **B** 84
- **C** 19,000
- **D** 30

151

About how many acres of pizza do Americans consume every day?

- **A** 10
- **B** 1,000
- **C** 10,000
- **D** 100

152

On average, every American man, woman and child consumes how many slices of pizza per year?

- **A** 3
- **B** 46
- **C** 19
- **D** 129

153

What's the favorite topping for pizza in America?

- **A** Pineapple
- **B** Pepperoni
- **C** Anchovies
- **D** Mushrooms

– Food for Thought –

How many days does the average American have to work in order to pay for their annual food bill?

154

- **A** 3
- **B** 208
- **C** 40
- **D** 98

What percentage of food in the US is thrown away every year?

155

- **A** 9%
- **B** 55%
- **C** 5%
- **D** 27%

How many M&Ms are produced every day?

156

- **A** 340,000,000
- **B** 10,000,000
- **C** 10,000
- **D** 12

157

The world record for drinking a pint of beer is what?

A 0.7 seconds
B 14 seconds
C 6 seconds
D 3 seconds

158

The world record for eating the most meatballs in one minute is what?

A 3
B 12
C 109
D 27

159

The record for swallowing sausages is how many sausages in a minute?

A 7
B 12
C 18
D 36

– Food for Thought –

The fine sport of blowing a marshmallow out of your nostril and having your partner catch it in their mouth is naturally a competitive one. What's the record distance for this admirable pastime?

- **A** 8 feet
- **B** 16 feet
- **C** 180 feet
- **D** 19 miles

The largest cocktail ever was mixed at Jimmy Buffett's Margaritaville in 2001. It was a margarita, of course, but just how large a margarita?

- **A** 7000 gallons
- **B** 500 gallons
- **C** 150 gallons
- **D** 15 gallons

The tallest Champagne pyramid ever successfully filled with Champagne contained how many glasses?

- **A** 30,856
- **B** 458
- **C** 122
- **D** 8,519

163 Which country produces the most fruit?

  A United States
  B India
  C China
  D South Africa

164 Which country produces the most coconuts?

  A Brazil
  B Jamaica
  C Indonesia
  D United States

165 Which country produces the most dates?

  A Egypt
  B Iran
  C Pakistan
  D Greece

– Food for Thought –

Which country produces the most chickens, goats, cabbages and walnuts?

166

- **A** United States
- **B** India
- **C** China
- **D** Russia

Which country consumes the most baked beans?

167

- **A** Mexico
- **B** United States
- **C** United Kingdom
- **D** Ireland

Which country consumes the most breakfast cereal per capita?

168

- **A** Canada
- **B** United Kingdom
- **C** United States
- **D** Sweden

169 Which country consumes the most frozen food per capita?

- **A** Alaska
- **B** United States
- **C** Norway
- **D** Iceland

170 Which country has the most fast food outlets?

- **A** Russia
- **B** China
- **C** United States
- **D** Australia

171 Which country consumes the most ice cream per capita?

- **A** Australia
- **B** United States
- **C** South Africa
- **D** United Kingdom

– Food for Thought –

Which of these countries is not joint first in the list of highest chewing gum consumers?

- **A** Andorra
- **B** Iceland
- **C** Norway
- **D** Finland

Which country consumes the most wine per head?

- **A** Italy
- **B** France
- **C** Spain
- **D** Luxembourg

Per capita, which country consumes the most alcohol?

- **A** United Kingdom
- **B** Ireland
- **C** Russia
- **D** United States

175 Who, per capita, are the biggest beer drinkers?

- **A** Ireland
- **B** Germany
- **C** Czech Republic
- **D** United States

176 Which country consumes more coffee per head than any other?

- **A** United States
- **B** France
- **C** Italy
- **D** Sweden

177 Which country consumes the most carbonated soft drinks per head?

- **A** Australia
- **B** China
- **C** United States
- **D** Japan

What's an amphora?

178

    A The bucket wine-tasters spit their wine into

    B An ancient vessel that was used to store wine

    C A wine glass with a curved lip

    D A wine thermometer

In what century did the great wine plague Phylloxera vastatrix threaten to destroy all of Europe's vineyards?

179

    A 3rd Century BC

    B 19th Century

    C 12th Century

    D 4th Century

A Salmanazar is equivalent to how many standard bottles of Champagne?

180

    A 2

    B 4

    C 12

    D 18

181

The following are all Champagne bottles. Which is the largest?

- **A** Balthazar
- **B** Jeroboam
- **C** Nebuchadnezzar
- **D** Methuselah

182

What's the name given to a Champagne bottle that holds the equivalent of six standard bottles of Champagne?

- **A** Magnum
- **B** Rehoboam
- **C** Jeroboam
- **D** Balthazar

183

A Bordeaux cork is how big?

- **A** 7/8 an inch
- **B** 3/4 of an inch
- **C** 1 1/2 inches
- **D** 3 1/8 inches

Which of these is a type of drinking vessel?

184

    A Parrapha
    B Poteen
    C Porron
    D Pesqaule

Queen Victoria favored wines from which country?

185

    A Germany
    B France
    C Chile
    D England

Alsace glasses often have which feature?

186

    A A green stem
    B A blue stem
    C A lead base
    D A lead handle

187

What did Queen Victoria like to mix with her Claret?

A Rum

B Tomato juice

C Water

D Whiskey

188

The Copita glass is traditionally associated with which drink?

A Sherry

B Champagne

C Port

D Brandy

189

What are heeltaps?

A Corks

B The stoppers that are used in oak barrels

C The dregs at the bottom of a wine glass

D Grapes rejected for wine making for being over-ripe

It takes the juice of roughly how many grapes to make a single bottle of wine?

190

A 20

B 7,000

C 1,500

D 600

A Black Velvet consists of —?

191

A White wine and blackcurrant

B Champagne and stout

C Tia Maria and Sherry

D Red wine and lime

How many bottles of wine went down with the Titanic?

192

A 20

B 21,000

C 400

D 1,500

193 What name is given to the small conical indentation at the bottom of a wine bottle?

- **A** A punt
- **B** A pop
- **C** A palart
- **D** A coney

194 What does Trocken mean on a bottle of German wine?

- **A** Dry
- **B** Sweet
- **C** Sparkling
- **D** Low in alcohol

195 What's the correct way to consume tequila?

- **A** Tequila – lemon – salt
- **B** Lemon – tequila – salt
- **C** Salt – tequila – lemon
- **D** Tequila – salt – lemon

– Leftovers –

What is Merchandise 7X?

196

A Captain Kirk's favorite food in Star Trek

B The secret formula of Coca-Cola

C Americas secret supply of tinned food, to be used in the event of a nuclear war

D The food astronauts take aboard the Space Shuttle

What is made from the roots of the blue agave cactus?

197

A Tequila

B Poteen

C Vodka

D Hummus

If you practice entomophagy you eat what?

198

A Only dairy products

B Tree bark

C Mud

D Insects

199 Strange cravings for unusual foods (such as those experienced by pregnant women) are called what?

A Munchies
B Bisca
C Palla
D Pica

200 The worlds most expensive jam, Confiture de Groselles, is what flavor?

A Redcurrant
B Truffle
C Blackberry
D Strawberry

201 What is the principal ingredient of halva?

A Sesame seeds
B Sunflower seeds
C Pumpkin seeds
D Mackerel

The average American eats how many pigs in their lifetime?

202

- **A** 9
- **B** 28
- **C** 46
- **D** 95

The first meal eaten in space was what?

203

- **A** Pecan nuts
- **B** Apple sauce
- **C** Cheese sandwiches
- **D** Rice crackers

Which of these is NOT used to make the anointing oil used at the coronation of British Kings and Queens?

204

- **A** Oranges
- **B** Cinnamon
- **C** Musk
- **D** Elderberries

205 From the milk of which animal is Roquefort cheese made?

A Sheep

B Goat

C Cow

D Buffalo

206 Which fruit has the most calories?

A Avocado

B Melon

C Kiwi

D Nectarine

207 What, on a Sushi menu, is tako?

A Seaweed

B Puffer fish

C Octopus

D Vine leaves

The word caviar comes from which country?

208

- **A** Russia
- **B** France
- **C** Egypt
- **D** Turkey

What's the most popular meal ordered in sit-down restaurants in the US?

209

- **A** Roast beef
- **B** Fried chicken
- **C** Spaghetti
- **D** Turkey

What meal is most requested by death row inmates before execution?

210

- **A** Steak and chips
- **B** Pizza
- **C** Cheeseburger
- **D** Toast

– Leftovers –

211 **Haggis is made from the stomach of which animal?**

   A Horse
   B Goat
   C Sheep
   D Sow

212 **What is boxty?**

   A Potato pancake
   B Fish soup
   C Leek pie
   D Cheese-flavored dessert

213 **The pigs used to hunt truffles are always what?**

   A Under five years old
   B Over five years old
   C Female
   D Male

What's the most widely-eaten fish in the world?

214

    A Cod

    B Haddock

    C Plaice

    D Herring

What do cheesemakers call the holes in cheese?

215

    A Warbles

    B Nodes

    C Eyes

    D Burrows

Cheese features in what percentage of British lunchboxes?

216

    A 5%

    B 16%

    C 32%

    D 64%

217

Which President was famous for his love of jelly bellies?

A Nixon

B Reagan

C Clinton

D Jefferson

218

Rennet, a key ingredient in most cheeses, comes from which part of a calf?

A The stomach

B The intestine

C The tongue

D The brain

219

Roughly how many berries do you need to make a pound of coffee?

A 100

B 2000

C 5000

D 10,000

– Leftovers –

What's the most popular ice cream topping in America? `220`

- **A** Butterscotch
- **B** Chocolate
- **C** Hot fudge
- **D** Strawberry

The nacatamal is made up of layers of meat and vegetables in banana leaves and is a common snack in which country? `221`

- **A** Ecuador
- **B** Nicaragua
- **C** Mexico
- **D** Indonesia

What percentage of cheese sold in England is Cheddar? `222`

- **A** 57%
- **B** 22%
- **C** 3%
- **D** 84%

223 What would you expect a Chicago sundae to taste of?

- **A** Pineapple
- **B** Apple
- **C** Blueberry
- **D** Peach

224 About how many crocus flowers does it take to produce one pound (0.5kg) of saffron?

- **A** 10
- **B** 75,000
- **C** 1,000
- **D** 100

225 Chili is the official state dish of where?

- **A** Texas
- **B** New Mexico
- **C** Louisiana
- **D** Kansas

– Leftovers –

What's the main ingredient in moussaka?
226

    A Leeks

    B Rabbit

    C Chicken

    D Aubergine (eggplant)

If you asked for a glass of beer in Ireland, what would you expect to be served?
227

    A A pint

    B A half a pint

    C A quarter of a pint

    D Two pints

What's the key ingredient in the cocktail Sea Breeze?
228

    A Rum

    B Whiskey

    C Vodka

    D Wine

229 Which of these is NOT a vitamin?

- **A** K
- **B** U
- **C** H
- **D** Z

230 About how many peanuts does it take to make a standard jar of peanut butter?

- **A** 5000
- **B** 50
- **C** 50,000
- **D** 500

231 What did Napoleon always carry with him on military campaigns?

- **A** Raisins
- **B** Gin
- **C** Chocolate
- **D** Figs

Coronation chicken is served how?

232

- **A** Raw
- **B** Cold
- **C** Warm
- **D** In a basket

In the film ET, what did Elliott use to lure the alien out into the open?

233

- **A** Flumps
- **B** Reese's Pieces
- **C** Jelly beans
- **D** M&Ms

In what year did the world get its first taste of a Snickers bar?

234

- **A** 1930
- **B** 1941
- **C** 1952
- **D** 1966

235 Who was directly responsible for the invention of margarine?

    A Queen Victoria

    B Napoleon

    C Winston Churchill

    D Thomas Jefferson

236 St Honorius is the patron saint of who?

    A Bakers

    B Cheesemakers

    C Waitresses

    D Farmers

237 St Laurence is the patron saint of who?

    A Diners

    B Poisoners

    C Wine makers

    D Cooks

Who is the patron saint of Fishmongers? **238**

- **A** St Peter
- **B** St Bona
- **C** St Cecilia
- **D** St Magnus

What food are more people allergic to than any other? **239**

- **A** Peanuts
- **B** Milk
- **C** Cheese
- **D** Honey

Where was the Caesar salad first served? **240**

- **A** France
- **B** Italy
- **C** Mexico
- **D** United States

241

When was the first Happy Hour?

- **A** 1899
- **B** 1914
- **C** 1945
- **D** 1960

242

What was the favorite drink of John F Kennedy and his wife Jacqueline?

- **A** Martini
- **B** Coffee with a shot or two of something stronger
- **C** Manhattan
- **D** Daiquiri

243

The name asparagus comes from which language?

- **A** Latin
- **B** Greek
- **C** Russian
- **D** French

– Leftovers –

What percentage of pumpkins are water?

- A 5%
- B 10%
- C 90%
- D 50%

Chinese brides are called by a word that translates as what?

- A Peach
- B Prune
- C Little apple
- D Pig

What oil is used for underwater cooking in submarines because it does not smoke unless heated above 450° F?

- A Olive
- B Peanut
- C Rapeseed
- D Sunflower

247 What is Arachbutyrophobia a morbid fear of?

- A Spiders getting in your food
- B Peanut butter sticking to the roof of your mouth
- C Not having enough bread for sandwiches
- D The smell of rancid milk

248 Who was the first person to market frozen food?

- A HJ Heinz
- B Clarence Birdseye
- C Jack Frost
- D James Blackwell

249 In 1765, John Montagu, the fourth Earl of Sandwich, invented the sandwich. The Earl used to order roast beef between pieces of toast for a snack while he was doing what?

- A Dining outdoors – he hated knives and forks
- B Out riding
- C Playing at the gaming tables; it allowed him to keep one hand free to play while he ate
- D Gardening

– Leftovers –

About how many apples does it take to make a glass of apple cider?

- **A** 150
- **B** 12
- **C** 25
- **D** 3

At the first Thanksgiving dinner, The Pilgrims ate what?

- **A** Popcorn
- **B** Ice cream
- **C** Curry
- **D** Caviar

What's the name of the basket of metal wire that keeps a champagne cork in place?

- **A** The clample
- **B** The crapple
- **C** The clasp
- **D** The coiffe

253 Wild rice is actually a type of —?

A Nut

B Herb

C Fish

D Grass

254 Norma's, at Le Parker Meridien hotel in New York, offers the most expensive single course dish in the world It retails at $1000 and is...

A An omelette

B A soup

C A risotto

D A stir-fry

255 What percentage of coffee sold in the UK is Fair Trade?

A 0.2%

B 3%

C 13%

D 53%

256

How many Fair Trade products are available in the UK?

- **A** 250
- **B** 80
- **C** 12
- **D** 3,900

257

A survey by Keep Britain Tidy in 2004 found that what percentage of English pavements have chewing gum stuck to them?

- **A** 66%
- **B** 18%
- **C** 7%
- **D** 94%

258

Wrap rage: in a survey by Yours magazine, a publication aimed at the over 50s in the UK, what percentage of readers claimed to have been injured whilst attempting to open food packaging?

- **A** 5%
- **B** 12%
- **C** 71%
- **D** 38%

259 How long did the illusionist David Blaine go without food in 2003 whilst suspended in a perspex box above Central London?

- A 9 days
- B 22 days
- C 44 days
- D 66 days

260 Which European country eats more potato snacks than the rest of Europe combined?

- A United Kingdom
- B Ireland
- C Germany
- D Spain

261 On average, how many bags of potato snacks does each person in the United Kingdom consume per year?

- A 5
- B 20
- C 150
- D 280

The five tastes are sweet, sour, salty, bitter and —?

262

A Spicy

B Addami

C Umami

D Cumaman

Which of these is NOT a type of cauliflower?

263

A Snowball

B Barrier Reef

C Autumn Giant

D White Dragon

Loch Ness, Blue Lake and Canadian Wonder are all types of what?

264

A Spinach

B Artichoke

C Bean

D Beetroot

265

Green Comet is a type of what?

A Cabbage

B Broccoli

C Lettuce

D Leek

266

Which of these is NOT a cabbage?

A Gypsy

B Best of All

C Jupiter

D Greyhound

267

Which of these is NOT a parsnip?

A Tender and True

B The Student

C Avonresister

D The Giddy Percival

– Leftovers –

The berries of what tree were used by ancient Egyptians to treat tapeworms?

268

- **A** Olive
- **B** Fig
- **C** Elder
- **D** Juniper

Vanilla comes from a plant from which family?

269

- **A** Foxglove
- **B** Orchid
- **C** Sunflower
- **D** Cucumber

A psomophagist is someone who does what?

270

- **A** Checks food for poisons
- **B** Starves himself to death
- **C** Bolts their food
- **D** Drinks urine

OTHER TITLES

There are many other exciting quiz
and puzzle books in the IntelliQuest range,
and your QUIZMO electronic unit
knows the answers to them all!

You can order from your
local bookshop or on-line bookseller.

For a full listing of current titles
(and ISBN numbers) see:

www.intelliquestbooks.com